UNIFIX

MATHEMATICS ACTIVITIES

BOOK 2

ADDITION – SUBTRACTION – PLACE VALUE
MULTIPLICATION – FRACTIONS – MEASUREMENT – STATISTICS

By
Don Balka

Didax
Educational Resources

Production Services: Group Four Resources
Editing and Layout: Dee Corr, Sherri Flaschner

ISBN 1-885111-01-0

H I J K   97 98 99

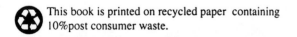
This book is printed on recycled paper containing 10%post consumer waste.

BACKGROUND

The structural mathematics manipulative material marketed under the name of Unifix® first made its appearance in Great Britain in 1952. Within two years it was being used extensively in the United States and Canada. The material was originated, designed, and patented by Charles A. Tacey, O.B.E.

Unifix®, a combination of plastic interlocking cubes and ancillary materials designed to enable the cubes to be used on a progressive scale, presents a challenging and positive basis for the exploration and expansion of understanding of early mathematics. Its principal value lies in its capacity to present the child with easily structured **concrete analogues** of the concepts of basic number relations and operations from which all mathematics, at all levels, derive.

It should be emphasized that Unifix® is not a rigid scheme or related to any prescriptive program. Primarily, it is a highly flexible and adaptable tool, capable of supporting cognitive and heuristic mathematics activity with meaning and self-evident proof.

CONTENTS

NOTES TO THE TEACHER

This book is organized around the basic mathematical concepts taught in kindergarten through fourth grade. Each activity lists recommended grade levels, focus concepts or skills, suggested number of students, and materials needed. Grade levels are intended as a general guide. Your knowledge of your students' abilities and current working levels should always be your primary guide. For your planning purposes, a list of Concept/Skills is presented below. Many of the activities are appropriate for independent use by the students. If teacher participation is required, it is stated after the "Number of Players." All Unifix support materials are given by catalog name to facilitate their identification when a product needs to be ordered.

The "Getting Ready" section details any necessary preparations for the activity. "Directions" are then given, followed by "Variations" for modifying activities. Some materials are items commonly found in the classroom. When an activity calls for copying a game, activity, or record sheet, a blackline master directly follows the activity description. These masters are suitable for reproduction on a duplicating machine or with a heat transfer process. All reproduced sheets can be made in classroom sets and used repeatedly. To promote stability and durability, it is recommended that you use card stock as the base, do any necessary cutting, and then laminate the final product.

CONCEPTS OR SKILLS

ACTIVITY 1 Addition with sums to 5 or 10

ACTIVITY 2 Addition with two-digit and one-digit addends

ACTIVITY 3 Addition, subtraction

ACTIVITY 4 Place value with ones and tens

ACTIVITY 5 Place value with ones and tens, number word recognition

ACTIVITY 6 Place value, addition

ACTIVITY 7 Place value, addition

ACTIVITY 8 Place value through hundreds, addition

ACTIVITY 9 Place value to 100 or 1000, addition

ACTIVITY 10 Beginning multiplication with arrays

ACTIVITY 11 Modeling basic multiplication facts

ACTIVITY 12 Multiplication with 2, 3, 4 and 5 as factors

ACTIVITY 13 Basic multiplication through product of 25

ACTIVITY 14 Multiplication through 10 x 10, multiples

ACTIVITY 15 Building models for fractions through sixths

ACTIVITY 16 Naming fractions, determining equivalent fractions

ACTIVITY 17 Estimation of length, measurement

ACTIVITY 18 Probability, graphing

ACTIVITY 19 Probability, graphing

ACTIVITY 20 Data collection, estimation, probability

INTRODUCTION

Since their appearance several years ago, Unifix Cubes and related Unifix support materials have been part of mathematics education throughout the world. The "structured" quality, bright colors, and durability of the Unifix Cubes provide an exciting appeal for young children during early mathematical learning.

Games and activities in this book focus on the child as an active participant in the learning process through physical manipulation of Unifix Cubes. Unlike many other books and manuals written for use with mathematics materials, this book provides ready-made game and activity sheets for a teacher to use in the classroom, along with a listing of appropriate grade levels, concepts or skills, number of students for the activity, materials needed, directions for getting ready to use the activity, directions for play, and suggestions for variations in play. Some duplicating, cutting, and coloring are necessary. Some Unifix support materials are needed for various activities; however, much of the material is contained in the book.

Since Unifix material is unit based, the activities cover a wide range of primary school mathematics. The first activities deal with addition and subtraction using one- or two-digit addends. Place value concepts through 1000 are covered by several small group games. Modeling of multiplication through arrays provides concrete representations for children. Similarly, building models of fractions with Unifix Cubes allows children to visualize a variety of notions about them. Probability and statistics via graphing have taken on added importance in today's mathematics curricula. The games and activities for these topics make graphing and interpretation of graphs easy.

A child's excitement in learning and understanding mathematics is a joy for all teachers. Hopefully, you will find the games and activities in this book to be a step in the right direction for providing that excitement.

Don S. Balka

ABOUT THE AUTHOR

Don S. Balka, Ph.D., is a noted mathematics educator who has presented numerous workshops on the use of math manipulatives with elementary school aged children at national and regional conferences of the National Council of Teachers of Mathematics and at in-service training for school districts throughout the United States. He has visited and taught classes in schools throughout Ireland, Scotland, and England, where Unifix materials are an integral part of the mathematics classroom.

NCTM STANDARDS

The activities in this book correlate with the *Curriculum and Evaluation Standards for School Mathematics* published by the National Council of Teachers of Mathematics in 1989. A correlation chart appears below.

STANDARD	1	2	3	4	5	6	7	8	9	10	11	12	13	14	15	16	17	18	19	20
1 Mathematics as Problem Solving																		■		
2 Mathematics as Communication	■			■	■	■				■	■	■	■	■	■	■				
3 Mathematics as Reasoning	■	■	■					■		■	■	■	■			■				
4 Mathematical Connections	■	■			■			■		■										
5 Estimation									■								■			
6 Number Sense and Numeration	■	■	■	■	■	■	■	■	■						■					
7 Concepts of Whole Number Operations	■	■	■	■			■	■	■	■	■	■	■	■						
8 Whole Number Computation	■	■	■				■		■	■	■	■	■	■		■		■	■	
9 Geometry and Spatial Sense		■																		
10 Measurements																■				
11 Statistics and Probability									■							■	■			
12 Fractions and Decimals														■	■					
13 Patterns and Relationships														■	■					

GRADE LEVEL: K - 2

CONCEPTS OR SKILLS:
Addition with sums to 5 or 10

NUMBER OF PLAYERS:
1 with teacher participation; small groups

MATERIALS:
20 Unifix Cubes of one color and
20 Cubes of a different color
Unifix Operational Grid and Tray
Unifix Blank Underlay Cards
Unifix Gummed Sheets (two
  colors) or
Unifix Wax crayons (two colors)
Unifix Gummed Sheets (+ and =)
Unifix Number Indicators
Unifix Gummed Sheets (1,2,3,4)

GETTING READY:
There are ten basic addition facts up to a sum of 5, excluding those involving 0 as an addend:

1 + 1, 1 + 2, 1 + 3, 1 + 4, 2 + 1,
2 + 2, 2 + 3, 3 + 1, 3 + 2, 4 + 1.

Using a Unifix Blank Underlay Card with the Gummed Squares, construct cards similar to the one shown below:

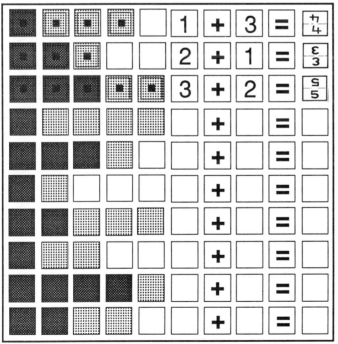

Mix the order of the number sentences on each card.

DIRECTIONS:
Ask the student to place Unifix Cubes on the Grid according to the colors shown for each row. Students find the sum by counting the number of cubes, and then place the corresponding Unifix Number Indicator on the grid to complete the number sentence.

Then ask questions such as:
How many ways are there to get a sum of 2?
How many ways are there to get a sum of 3?
How many ways are there to get a sum of 4?
How many ways are there to get a sum of 5?

VARIATIONS:
For students working on basic facts up to sums of 10, construct cards containing five number sentences with sums up to 10. Students place Unifix Cubes on the Grid and find the sum as before.

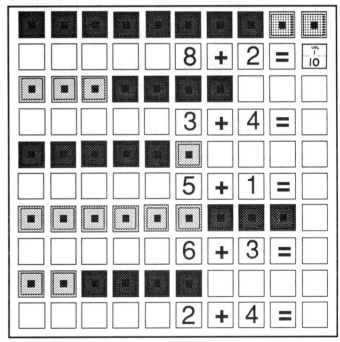

In a game format with a small group, each player needs a Unifix Operational Grid and Tray with a card (sums to 10) and several Unifix Cubes of two colors. A 0 to 9 Spinner Sheet and Spinner are also needed for each group. During his or her turn, a player spins the spinner and covers all squares where the number shown is an addend. If a player spins a number (addend) that has already been covered, he or she loses that turn. If a player spins a 0, he or she loses that turn. As a player covers a particular row, he or she places the correct Unifix Number Indicator on the grid to complete the number sentence. The winner is the first player to correctly complete five number sentences.

GRADE LEVEL: 2 - 3

CONCEPTS OR SKILLS:
Addition with two-digit and one-digit addends, subtraction

NUMBER OF PLAYERS: 2

MATERIALS:
50 Unifix Cubes for each player
Unifix 100 Track (first five sections) for each player
1 to 10 Spinner Sheet and a spinner
Track Race Record Sheet

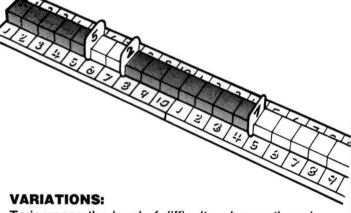

GETTING READY:

Connect the first five sections of the Unifix 100 Track for each player.

A 1 to 10 Spinner Sheet and spinner are needed for each pair of players.

A Track Race Record Sheet is needed for each pair of players. After initial practice, cover the numbers on the 100 Track with masking tape.

DIRECTIONS:

During a player's first turn, he or she spins the spinner and places the corresponding number of Unifix Cubes on the track as a structured bar. The player records the addend on the Record Sheet as shown.

TRACK RACE RECORD SHEET					
Game 1			**Game 2**		
SPIN		ADDEND	SPIN		ADDEND
1		5	1		___
2		2	2		___
	SUM	7		SUM	___
3		3	3		___
	SUM	10		SUM	___
4		2	4		___
	SUM	12		SUM	___
5			5		

Continuing, each player spins the spinner and adds the corresponding number of Unifix Cubes to the previous structured bar. The player records the second addend on the Record Sheet and writes the sum corresponding to the "new" structured bar.

The first player to reach a sum of 50 or more by filling the track with cubes is the winner.

VARIATIONS:

To increase the level of difficulty, change the rules so that a player must get exactly 50. If a player spins a number which will give a sum over 50, he or she loses that turn.

Subtraction: To start, each player fills the track with 50 cubes. During his or her turn, a player spins the spinner and removes the corresponding number of cubes from the track. The player then records the subtraction number sentence and the resulting difference as shown on the track. The first player to reach exactly 0 is the winner. A player loses a turn if a number cannot be subtracted without getting a negative difference.

TRACK RACE RECORD SHEET

Game 1

SPIN		ADDEND
1		_____
2		_____
	SUM	_____
3		_____
	SUM	_____
4		_____
	SUM	_____
5		_____
	SUM	_____
6		_____
	SUM	_____
7		_____
	SUM	_____
8		_____
	SUM	_____
9		_____
	SUM	_____
10		_____
	SUM	_____

Game 2

SPIN		ADDEND
1		_____
2		_____
	SUM	_____
3		_____
	SUM	_____
4		_____
	SUM	_____
5		_____
	SUM	_____
6		_____
	SUM	_____
7		_____
	SUM	_____
8		_____
	SUM	_____
9		_____
	SUM	_____
10		_____
	SUM	_____

Didax Educational Resources, Inc.

> **GRADE LEVEL:** 2 - 4
>
> **CONCEPTS OR SKILLS:**
> Addition, subtraction
>
> **NUMBER OF PLAYERS:**
> Small groups
>
> **MATERIALS:**
> Unifix Operational Grid and Tray for each player
> 1 to 100 Underlay for each player
> Several Unifix Cubes for each player
> 1 to 100 Cards or One to One Hundred Cards

GETTING READY:

Make copies of the 1 to 100 cards or One to One Hundred cards on card stock and cut them apart.

Each group needs a deck of cards.

Each player needs a Unifix Operational Grid and Tray, a 1 to 100 Underlay Card, and several Unifix Cubes.

DIRECTIONS:

Subtraction

During his or her turn, each player draws two cards from the deck, places them on the table, mentally subtracts the smaller number from the larger number, and covers the number that equals the difference on the grid. The player then discards the two cards. If a player subtracts incorrectly, then the player next in order of play who answers correctly places a cube on the correct difference. If a player draws two numbers whose difference has already been covered, he or she loses that turn.

Addition

For an addition game, use only cards from 1 to 50.

During his or her turn, a player draws two cards, places them on the table, mentally computes the sum of the two numbers, and covers the number on the grid that equals the sum . The player then

discards the two cards. If a player adds incorrectly, the player next in order of play who answers correctly places a cube on the appropriate sum. If a player draws two numbers whose sum has already been covered, the player loses that turn.

The winner for either game is the first player to get three cubes in a row, horizontally, vertically or diagonally.

VARIATIONS:

The group can play using just one Unifix Operational Grid and Tray, with each player using a different color of Unifix Cubes.

The duration of the game can be increased by requiring that five cubes be placed in a row, horizontally, vertically or diagonally in order to win or the winner can be the player with the most cubes on the grid.

In case of ties, the player with the greatest sum for addition or least difference for subtraction is the winner.

Rather than losing a turn when a sum or difference has already been covered, allow players to stack cubes on the number. A winner can now set three in a stack.

1 TO 100 CARDS

1	2	3
4	5	6
7	8	9
10	11	12
13	14	15
16	17	18

1 TO 100 CARDS

19	**20**	**21**
22	**23**	**24**
25	**26**	**27**
28	**29**	**30**
31	**32**	**33**
34	**35**	**36**

1 TO 100 CARDS

37	38	39
40	41	42
43	44	45
46	47	48
49	50	51
52	53	54

1 TO 100 CARDS

55	56	57
58	59	60
61	62	63
64	65	66
67	68	69
70	71	72

1 TO 100 CARDS

73	**74**	**75**
76	**77**	**78**
79	**80**	**81**
82	**83**	**84**
85	**86**	**87**
88	**89**	**90**

1 TO 100 CARDS

91	**92**	**93**
94	**95**	**96**
97	**98**	**99**
100	**1 TO 100 CARDS**	

ONE TO ONE HUNDRED CARDS

ONE	TWO	THREE
FOUR	FIVE	SIX
SEVEN	EIGHT	NINE
TEN	ELEVEN	TWELVE
THIRTEEN	FOURTEEN	FIFTEEN
SIXTEEN	SEVENTEEN	EIGHTEEN

Didax Educational Resources, Inc.

ONE TO ONE HUNDRED CARDS

NINETEEN	**TWENTY**	**TWENTY-ONE**
TWENTY-TWO	**TWENTY-THREE**	**TWENTY-FOUR**
TWENTY-FIVE	**TWENTY-SIX**	**TWENTY-SEVEN**
TWENTY-EIGHT	**TWENTY-NINE**	**THIRTY**
THIRTY-ONE	**THIRTY-TWO**	**THIRTY-THREE**
THIRTY-FOUR	**THIRTY-FIVE**	**THIRTY-SIX**

Didax Educational Resources, Inc.

ONE TO ONE HUNDRED CARDS

THIRTY-SEVEN	**THIRTY-EIGHT**	**THIRTY-NINE**
FORTY	**FORTY-ONE**	**FORTY-TWO**
FORTY-THREE	**FORTY-FOUR**	**FORTY-FIVE**
FORTY-SIX	**FORTY-SEVEN**	**FORTY-EIGHT**
FORTY-NINE	**FIFTY**	**FIFTY-ONE**
FIFTY-TWO	**FIFTY-THREE**	**FIFTY-FOUR**

ONE TO ONE HUNDRED CARDS

FIFTY-FIVE	**FIFTY-SIX**	**FIFTY-SEVEN**
FIFTY-EIGHT	**FIFTY-NINE**	**SIXTY**
SIXTY-ONE	**SIXTY-TWO**	**SIXTY-THREE**
SIXTY-FOUR	**SIXTY-FIVE**	**SIXTY-SIX**
SIXTY-SEVEN	**SIXTY-EIGHT**	**SIXTY-NINE**
SEVENTY	**SEVENTY-ONE**	**SEVENTY-TWO**

Didax Educational Resources, Inc.

ONE TO ONE HUNDRED CARDS

SEVENTY-THREE	SEVENTY-FOUR	SEVENTY-FIVE
SEVENTY-SIX	SEVENTY-SEVEN	SEVENTY-EIGHT
SEVENTY-NINE	EIGHTY	EIGHTY-ONE
EIGHTY-TWO	EIGHTY-THREE	EIGHTY-FOUR
EIGHTY-FIVE	EIGHTY-SIX	EIGHTY-SEVEN
EIGHTY-EIGHT	EIGHTY-NINE	NINETY

ONE TO ONE HUNDRED CARDS

NINETY-ONE	**NINETY-TWO**	**NINETY-THREE**
NINETY-FOUR	**NINETY-FIVE**	**NINETY-SIX**
NINETY-SEVEN	**NINETY-EIGHT**	**NINETY-NINE**
ONE HUNDRED	**ONE TO ONE HUNDRED CARDS**	

BUILD TO TEN

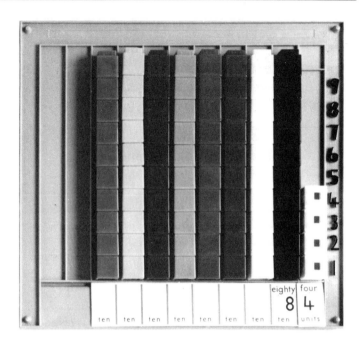

GRADE LEVEL: 1 - 2

CONCEPTS OR SKILLS:
Place value with ones and tens

NUMBER OF PLAYERS:
Small groups

MATERIALS:
Unifix Cubes for each group
Unifix Tens Cubes for each group
1 to 6 Spinner Sheet and a spinner
Unifix Dual Number Board
Unifix 20-100 Notation Cards

GETTING READY:
Each group needs Unifix Cubes and Unifix Tens Cubes and a 1 to 6 Spinner Sheet and spinner.

DIRECTIONS:
During his or her turn, each player spins the spinner and selects the corresponding number of Unifix Cubes and makes a structured bar. On succeeding turns each player combines the cubes with the structured bar from earlier turns. As soon as a player constructs a bar containing ten cubes, it is set aside. After five rounds, each player writes and/or states his or her total number of cubes. The winner is the player who has the most cubes at the end of the five rounds.

VARIATIONS:
For students having difficulty with the notion of ten, use the Unifix Dual Number Board so that students can place cubes in the channels of the board to see the structured bars of ten cubes.

Players can place the corresponding Unifix Notation Cards at the bottom of the board after each turn as shown.

For students at a higher developmental level, provide Unifix Tens Cubes. After a player constructs a structured bar of ten cubes, he or she can trade the bar for a Unifix Tens Cube.

GRADE LEVEL: 1 - 2

CONCEPTS OR SKILLS:
Place value with ones and tens, number word recognition

NUMBER OF PLAYERS:
Small groups or entire class with teacher participation

MATERIALS:
Ten Unifix Cubes for each player
Ten Unifix Tens Cubes for each player
Unifix One-Ten and Ones Tray for each player
1 to 100 Cards
One to One Hundred Cards

GETTING READY:
Make copies of the 1 to 100 Cards or the One to One Hundred Cards on card stock and cut them apart.

Each player needs ten Unifix Cubes, ten Unifix Tens Cubes, and a Unifix One-Ten and Ones Tray.

DIRECTIONS:
Use the 1 to 100 card deck or the One to One Hundred card deck. Do not use the 100 or One Hundred card.

You, or a designated student, should draw a card from the deck and show it to the students. Each student fills the Unifix One-Ten and Ones Tray to illustrate the number shown. You can visually check trays or demonstrate the correct amount on a tray. Students then remove the cubes from their trays and a different number is drawn.

VARIATIONS:
Mix the two decks of cards and draw from the combined deck.

For place value concepts involving hundreds, make additional cards showing numbers like 258, 326, 438, or 936. Students will need a Unifix Hundreds, Tens and Ones Place Value Tray and Ten Unifix Hundreds Cubes. Again, you, or a student, should draw a number card and each student fills his or her tray illustrating that number.

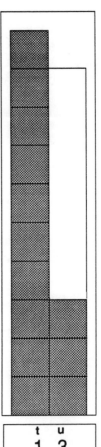

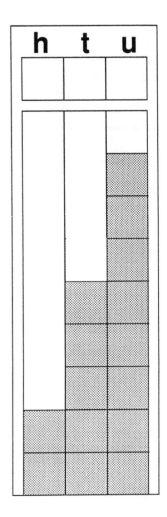

GRADE LEVEL: 2 - 3

CONCEPTS OR SKILLS:
Place value, addition

NUMBER OF PLAYERS:
2 or small groups

MATERIALS:
Twenty Unifix Cubes for each player
Ten Unifix Tens Cubes for each player
Unifix One-Ten and Ones Tray for each player
1 to 10 Spinner Sheet and a spinner

GETTING READY:

Each player needs twenty Unifix Cubes, ten Unifix Tens Cubes, and a Unifix One-Ten and Ones Tray.

Each group needs a 1 to 10 Spinner Sheet and a spinner.

DIRECTIONS:

During his or her turn, a player spins the spinner and places the corresponding number of cubes in the ones channel of the tray. As the game progresses, a trade may be necessary before placing additional cubes in the tray. For example, if a player has a tens cube in the tens channel and seven cubes in the ones channel and spins a 6, then a trade is required. The player fills the ones channel and then makes a trade of ten Unifix Cubes for one Unifix Tens Cube. The Unifix Tens Cube is placed in the tens channel and the remaining three cubes are placed in the ones channel. The resulting number is 23. The first player to fill the tray with ten Tens Cubes (100) is the winner.

VARIATIONS:

As a variation, require the winning player to have exactly 100 with no ones cubes in the ones channel.

For checking purposes, have players keep a record sheet for each game. As a player spins, he or she also writes the corresponding number sentence. For example:

6	13	15
+ 7	+ 2	+ 9
13	15	24
24	30	38
+ 6	+ 8	+ 3
30	38	41
41	46	50
+ 5	+ 4	+10
46	50	60

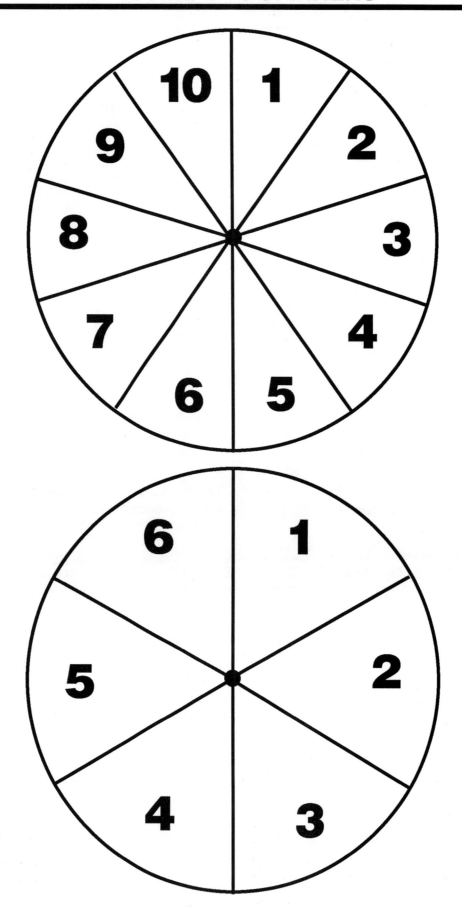

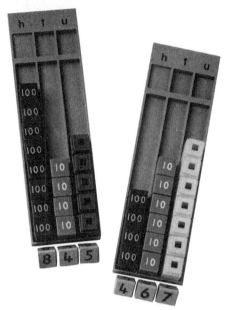

GRADE LEVEL: 2 - 3

CONCEPTS OR SKILLS:
Place value, addition

NUMBER OF PLAYERS:
Small groups

MATERIALS:
Ten Unifix Cubes for each player
Ten Unifix Tens Cubes for each player
Ten Unifix Hundreds Cubes for each player
Unifix Hundreds, Tens and Ones Place Value
Tray for each player
1 to 100 cards

GETTING READY:
Make copies of the 1 to 100 cards on card stock and cut them apart.

Each player needs ten Unifix Cubes, ten Unifix Tens Cubes, ten Unifix Hundreds Cubes and a Unifix Hundreds, Tens and Ones Place Value Tray.

DIRECTIONS:
Shuffle the cards and place them in front of the players.

During his or her turn, a player draws a card from the deck, selects the appropriate Unifix Cubes and places them in the proper channels of the tray.

As the game progresses, it will be necessary to trade cubes. As the players fill the ones channel, they trade ten unit cubes for a Tens Cube, and as the tens channel is filled, the ten Tens Cubes are traded for a Hundred Cube. For example, if a player has 268 showing on his or her tray, and he or she draws 79, then two trades are required. First, the ones channel is filled with the player trading ten Unifix Cubes for one Unifix Tens Cube. Seven cubes now remain in the ones channel.

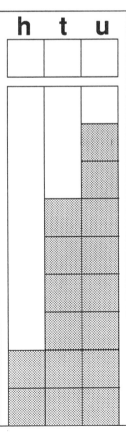

Next, the tens channel is filled with the player now trading ten Unifix Tens Cubes for one Unifix Hundreds Cube. Four Unifix Tens Cubes remain in the tens channel, and three Unifix Hundreds Cubes are now in the hundreds channel. The resulting number is 347.

The card is placed in a discard pile and the next player draws.

The winner is the first player to fill his tray with 1000 or more.

VARIATIONS:
For checking purposes, instruct players to keep a record sheet for each game. As a player draws a number card, he or she also performs the computation with paper and pencil. For example:

38	92	159
+54	+67	+22
92	159	181

181	268
+ 87	+79
268	347

347	443
+ 96	+75
443	518

GRADE LEVEL: 2 - 4

CONCEPTS OR SKILLS:
Place value through hundreds, addition

NUMBER OF PLAYERS:
Small groups

MATERIALS:
Paper bag containing Unifix Cubes of one
color
Unifix Tens Cubes, and Unifix Hundreds
Cubes. The number of cubes in the bag
should be sufficient for each player to draw
five cubes.
Number Power Activity Sheet for each player

GETTING READY:
Make a copy of the Number Power Activity Sheet
for each player.

Place Unifix Cubes of a single color, Unifix Tens
Cubes, and Unifix Hundreds Cubes in a paper bag.

Initially, you should show the students how to
record numbers for each of the five rounds of a
game.

DIRECTIONS:
During his or her first turn, each player takes one
cube from the bag and places it in the corresponding column of the activity sheet.

The player then writes the corresponding number
on the line for Round 1.

After each round, players should compare numbers.
Who has the largest number? Who has the smallest number?

Play continues for five rounds. Cubes from preced-
ing rounds remain on the activity sheet, and players
record the cumulative sum of all cubes on their
activity sheets. For example, if Player A takes a
Hundreds Cube in Round 1, a Tens Cube in Round
2, and a Hundreds Cube in Round 3, he or she
records the number 210 for Round 3.

The winner is the player who has the greatest sum
after five rounds.

VARIATIONS:
Reverse the rules so that the winner is the player
with the smallest number after five rounds.

Extend the game to ten or more rounds so that
trading may be necessary.

NUMBER POWER ACTIVITY SHEET

HUNDREDS	TENS	ONES
100	10	
100		

Game 1	Game 2	Game 3	Game 4
ROUND 1: _100_	ROUND 1: _____	ROUND 1: _____	ROUND 1: _____
ROUND 2: _110_	ROUND 2: _____	ROUND 2: _____	ROUND 2: _____
ROUND 3: _210_	ROUND 3: _____	ROUND 3: _____	ROUND 3: _____
ROUND 4: _____	ROUND 4: _____	ROUND 4: _____	ROUND 4: _____
ROUND 5: _____	ROUND 5: _____	ROUND 5: _____	ROUND 5: _____

NUMBER POWER ACTIVITY SHEET

HUNDREDS   TENS   ONES

Game 1	Game 2	Game 3	Game 4
ROUND 1: _____	ROUND 1: _____	ROUND 1: _____	ROUND 1: _____
ROUND 2: _____	ROUND 2: _____	ROUND 2: _____	ROUND 2: _____
ROUND 3: _____	ROUND 3: _____	ROUND 3: _____	ROUND 3: _____
ROUND 4: _____	ROUND 4: _____	ROUND 4: _____	ROUND 4: _____
ROUND 5: _____	ROUND 5: _____	ROUND 5: _____	ROUND 5: _____

Didax Educational Resources, Inc.

GRADE LEVEL: 1 - 3

CONCEPTS OR SKILLS:
Place value to 100 or 1000, addition

NUMBER OF PLAYERS:
Small groups

MATERIALS:
Unifix Cubes of one color, Unifix Tens Cubes, and Unifix Hundreds Cubes for each group
Unifix One-Ten and Ones Tray or Unifix Hundreds, Tens and Ones Place Value Tray for each player
1 to 6 Spinner Sheet and a spinner
1 and 10 Spinner Sheet and a spinner
1, 10 and 100 Spinner Sheet and a spinner

GETTING READY:
Make copies of the 1 to 6 Spinner Sheet for each group.

Make copies of the 1 and 10 or 1, 10 and 100 Spinner Sheet for each group.

Each player needs a Unifix One-Ten and Ones Tray or Hundreds, Tens and Ones Place Value Tray, depending upon which game is played.

DIRECTIONS:
Game 1 involves place value to 100; Game 2 involves place value to 1000.

Game 1. Use the 1 and 10 Spinner Sheet and the Unifix One-Ten and Ones Tray, along with the 1 to 6 Spinner Sheet.

During his or her turn, each player spins both spinners. The number on the 1 and 10 Spinner Sheet indicates place value. The resulting number on

the 1 to 6 Spinner Sheet indicates how many cubes should be selected.

For example, if the 1 to 6 Spinner Sheet shows a 3 and the 1 and 10 Spinner Sheet shows a 10, then the player selects 3 Unifix Tens Cubes and places them on the tray in the corresponding tens channel.

As the game progresses, players trade 10 cubes for one Tens Cube. For example, if there are 8 cubes in the ones channel and 4 cubes are added, then the player trades 10 cubes for a Tens Cube and 2 cubes remain in the ones channel. The winner is the first player to reach 100 or more.

Game 2. Use the 1, 10, and 100 Spinner Sheet and the Unifix Hundreds, Tens, and Ones Tray, along with the 1 to 6 Spinner Sheet.

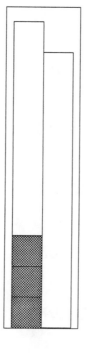

During his or her turn, a player spins both spinners. The number on the 1, 10 and 100 Spinner Sheet indicates the place value. The number on the 1 to 6 Spinner Sheet indicates how many cubes should be selected for that value. As in Game 1, the selected cubes are placed in the corresponding channel of the tray. Trades are made if necessary: One Tens Cube for 10 cubes, One Hundreds Cube for 10 Tens Cubes. The winner is the first player to reach 1000 or more.

VARIATIONS:
Change the rules so that to win a player must reach exactly 100 or 1000.

Ask students to keep a tally of how many turns are used to reach 100 or 1000.

Ask students to graph the resulting number of turns using Unifix Cubes. Then follow up by questioning students about their graphs:

1. What was the least number of turns?
2. What was the greatest number of turns?
3. About how many turns are usually needed to win?

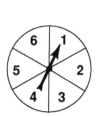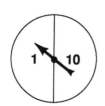

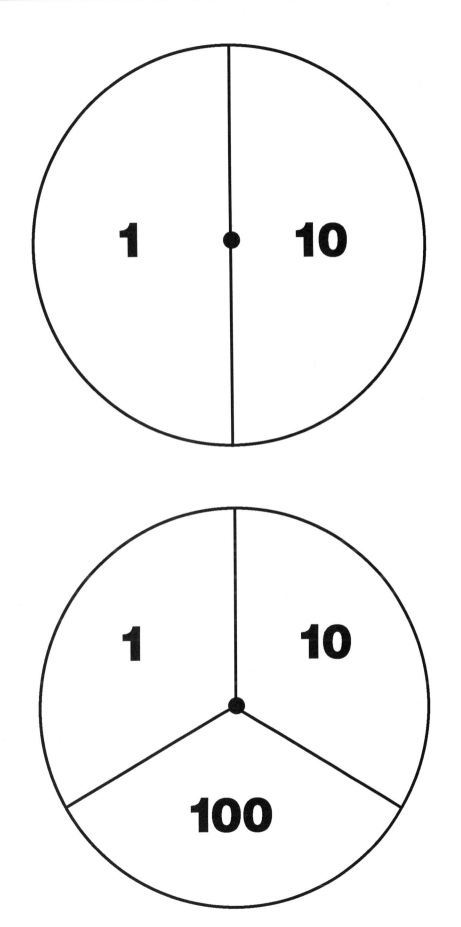

GRADE LEVEL: 3 - 4

CONCEPTS OR SKILLS:
Beginning multiplication with arrays

NUMBER OF PLAYERS: 1

MATERIALS:
Unifix Cubes of the same color
Unifix Operational Grid and Tray
Unifix Blank Underlay Cards
Unifix Number Indicators
Unifix Gummed Sheets for 1 - 9, x, =

GETTING READY:

Using the Unifix Blank Underlay Cards, construct several open multiplication number sentences with the gummed squares. Be sure to leave room for students to construct the cube arrays for each problem. Skip a row between each problem. An example is shown below.

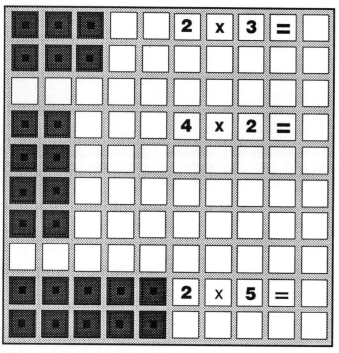

Place the completed card in a Unifix Operational Tray and cover with a grid.

DIRECTIONS:

Ask the student to construct rectangular arrays of Unifix Cubes on the Grid corresponding to the multiplication sentence on the right side. For example, a model of 2 x 3 gives two rows of cubes with three cubes in each row.

The student determines each product and places the corresponding Number Indicator on the grid to complete the number sentence.

You will need to check the products shown on the grid.

VARIATIONS:

After initial work with multiplication, construct Unifix Underlay Cards that incorporate 0 as a factor.

Construct Underlay Cards with the open multiplication sentences in vertical form.

Construct Underlay Cards with open multiplication sentences showing commutativity, such as 2 x 3 = 6 and 3 x 2 = 6.

PRODUCT BINGO

GRADE LEVEL: 2 - 4

CONCEPTS OR SKILLS:
Modeling basic multiplication facts

NUMBER OF PLAYERS:
Small groups or entire class, with teacher participation

MATERIALS:
Unifix Operational Grid and Tray for each player
Unifix Blank Underlay Card for each player
45 Unifix Cubes of one color for each player
Multiplication Cards

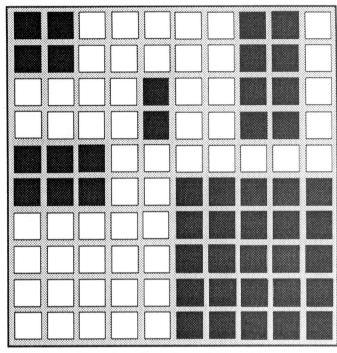

$$2 + 4 + 6 + 8 + 25 = 45$$

GETTING READY:
Make copies of the Multiplication Cards on card stock and cut them apart.

Combine two sets of cards into a single deck for Product Bingo.

Using the Unifix Blank Underlay Cards, construct several Product Bingo game cards by shading five rectangular arrays. Other possible configurations are presented. The sum of the five products for each card is 45. Additional cards can be made with different configurations.

$$2 + 4 + 6 + 8 + 25 = 45$$

$$1 + 4 + 9 + 15 + 16 = 45$$

$$2 + 5 + 6 + 12 + 20 = 45$$

$$3 + 4 + 8 + 10 + 20 = 45$$

$$4 + 5 + 8 + 12 + 16 = 45$$

$$3 + 5 + 10 + 12 + 15 = 45$$

$$1 + 6 + 8 + 10 + 20 = 45$$

$$2 + 3 + 5 + 10 + 25 = 45$$

$$3 + 4 + 6 + 12 + 20 = 45$$

$$2 + 4 + 9 + 15 + 15 = 45$$

Each child needs a Unifix Operational Grid and Tray with a Product Bingo card and 45 Unifix Cubes of one color.

DIRECTIONS:
You, or a designated student, should draw a Multiplication Card and show it to the group.

If a rectangular array corresponding to the product of the Multiplication Card is on a player's Product Bingo card, he or she covers the array with Unifix Cubes. Then ask the player to state the product.

The winner is the first player to cover all five arrays and correctly state the corresponding products.

VARIATIONS:
After students have practiced on basic multiplication facts, allow them to cover, if possible, an array with the same product. For example, if 3 x 4 is drawn, students could cover 4 x 3, 2 x 6, or 6 x 2.

For a variation, construct a deck of cards showing only the products. Students cover a rectangular array corresponding to the product.

Extend Product Bingo to higher factors.

MULTIPLICATION CARDS

1 x 1	**2 x 2**	**3 x 3**
1 x 2	**2 x 3**	**3 x 4**
1 x 3	**2 x 4**	**3 x 5**
1 x 4	**2 x 5**	**4 x 1**
1 x 5	**3 x 1**	**4 x 2**
2 x 1	**3 x 2**	**4 x 3**

MULTIPLICATION CARDS

4 x 4	**5 x 5**	
4 x 5		
5 x 1		
5 x 2		
5 x 3		
5 x 4		

GRADE LEVEL: 3 - 4

CONCEPTS OR SKILLS:
Multiplication with 2, 3, 4 and 5 as factors

NUMBER OF PLAYERS:
Small groups

MATERIALS:
Unifix Operational Grid and Tray for each
   player
Several Unifix Cubes of one color for each
   player
Unifix Blank Underlay Card for each player
Three Sets of Multiplication Cards for each
   group

GETTING READY:

Make copies of the Multiplication Cards on card
stock and cut them apart. Create a deck consisting
of three sets of Multiplication Cards.

Shade Unifix Underlay Cards to provide "four
corners" as illustrated below.

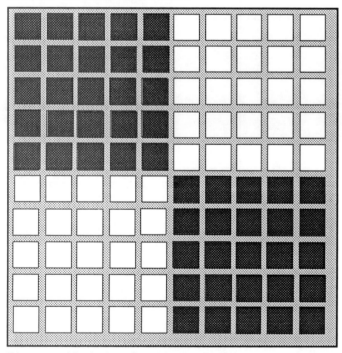

Place an Underlay Card in each tray.

DIRECTIONS:

During his or her turn, a player draws a Multiplication Card and constructs the corresponding rectangular array model with Unifix Cubes in one of the
four corners of the Operational Grid. The player
then states the resulting multiplication sentence.

Play continues for four rounds so that all four
corners of each player's grid are filled.

If a player gives an incorrect multiplication
sentence, his or her score for that round is 0.

After four rounds, each player counts the total
number of cubes on the tray.

The winner is the player who has the most cubes
on his or her tray.

STACK 'EM UP

GRADE LEVEL: 2 - 4

CONCEPTS OR SKILLS:
Basic multiplication through product of 25

NUMBER OF PLAYERS:
Small groups

MATERIALS:
Unifix Cubes for each player
Stack 'em Up game sheet for each player
0 to 5 Spinner Sheet and a spinner

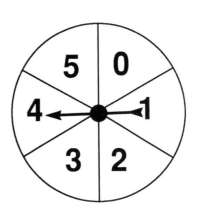

Game 1

$1 \times \underline{3} = \underline{3}$

$2 \times \underline{2} = \underline{4}$

$3 \times \underline{5} = \underline{15}$

$4 \times \underline{0} = \underline{0}$

$5 \times \underline{1} = \underline{5}$

Sum $\quad 27$

GETTING READY:
Make copies of the Stack 'em Up game sheet for each player.

Each player needs Unifix Cubes of the same color.

Each group needs a 0 to 5 Spinner Sheet and spinner.

DIRECTIONS:
During his or her first turn, each player spins the spinner and stacks the corresponding number of cubes on the activity sheet. The player then records the resulting multiplication number sentence on the sheet. For example, 1 x 3 = 3. The game continues in the same manner for five rounds. If on the fourth round, for example, a player spins a 5, he or she stacks four groups of five cubes in the corresponding area of the game sheet and records 4 x 5 = 20.

After five rounds have been completed, each player finds the sum of the five products, as shown.

The winner is the player with the greatest sum.

VARIATIONS:
Rather than proceeding in order, 1 through 5, allow players to select where they want to place the structured bars for each round.

Game 1

1 x _____ = _____

2 x _____ = _____

3 x _____ = _____

4 x _____ = _____

5 x _____ = _____

Sum _____

Game 2

1 x _____ = _____

2 x _____ = _____

3 x _____ = _____

4 x _____ = _____

5 x _____ = _____

Sum _____

Game 3

1 x _____ = _____

2 x _____ = _____

3 x _____ = _____

4 x _____ = _____

5 x _____ = _____

Sum _____

Didax Educational Resources, Inc.

0 - 5 SPINNER

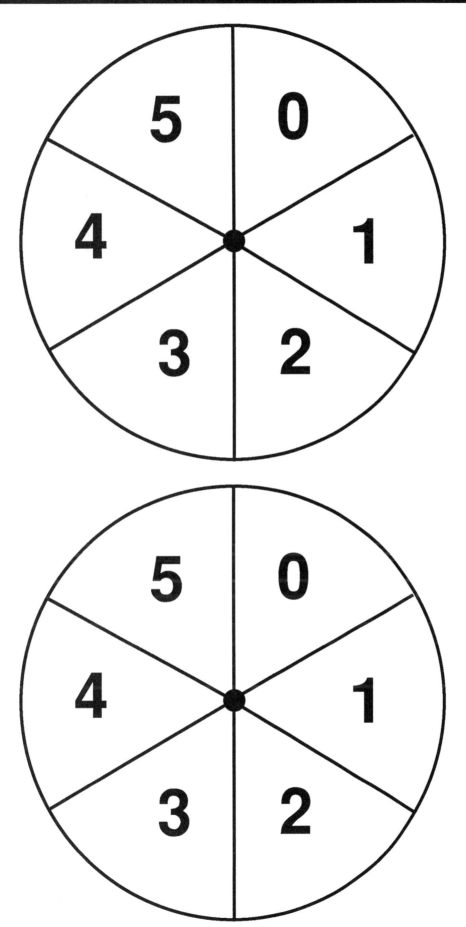

1	2	3	4	5	6	7	8	9	10
2	4	6	8	10	12	14	16	18	20
3	6	9	12	15	18	21	24	27	30
4	8	12	16	20	24	28	32	36	40
5	10	15	20	25	30	35	40	45	50
6	12	18	24	30	36	42	48	54	60
7	14	21	28	35	42	49	56	63	70
8	16	24	32	40	48	56	64	72	80
9	18	27	36	45	54	63	72	81	90
10	20	30	40	50	60	70	80	90	100

GRADE LEVEL: 3 - 4

CONCEPTS OR SKILLS:
Multiplication through 10 x 10, multiples

NUMBER OF PLAYERS:
Small groups

MATERIALS:
Unifix Cubes for each player
Unifix Operational Grid and Tray for each player
Unifix 1 to 100 Underlay Card (Table Square side)
Two 1 to 10 Spinner Sheets and a spinner for each group

GETTING READY:
Each player needs Unifix Cubes of one color, a Unifix Operational Grid and Tray, and a Unifix 1 to 100 Card. Players should use the reverse side of the card showing multiples.

Each group needs two 1 to 10 Spinner Sheets and spinners.

One spinner is designated the "multiple" spinner. The second spinner indicates the number of multiples.

DIRECTIONS:
During his or her turn, each player spins the first spinner indicating the multiple. This number designates the row on the grid sheet. The player then spins the second spinner. The number showing designates how many multiples of the number to cover. For example, if the first spinner shows a 7 and the second spinner shows a 5, the player places Unifix Cubes on 7, 14, 21, 28, and 35.

If a player spins a multiple that has already been used, he or she loses that turn. Play continues for 10 rounds. The winner is the player with the most cubes on the grid after 10 rounds.

VARIATIONS:
Construct a set of cards with the multiples shown on the grid.

During his or her turn, each player draws a card and spins one spinner. If the number on the card is a multiple of the number on the spinner, the player covers all the squares to the multiple. For example, if a player draws 36 and spins 4, he or she covers the multiples of 4 through 36.

Ask students to state the corresponding division sentence for each turn. For the example above, 36 ÷ 4 = 9.

The winner is the player with the most cubes after 10 rounds.

GRADE LEVEL: 2 - 4

CONCEPTS OR SKILLS:
Building models for fractions through sixths

NUMBER OF PLAYERS:
Small groups or entire class, with teacher participation

MATERIALS:
Six Unifix Cubes of one color and six Unifix Cubes of a different color for each player
Card Shark Fraction cards
Unifix Operational Grid and Tray
Unifix Blank Underlay Card for each player

GETTING READY:
Make copies of the Card Shark fraction cards on card stock and cut them apart.

Each player needs a total of twelve Unifix Cubes of two different colors.

Each player needs a Unifix Operational Grid and Tray and a Blank Underlay Card.

DIRECTIONS:
To begin, show a Card Shark Fraction card to the entire group or class. Each player constructs on the grid a corresponding model representing the fraction. For example, if $\frac{3}{4}$ is shown, students might use three red Unifix Cubes and one white Unifix Cube. You may want to designate what colors to use.

In a game format for small groups of two or three players, combine three sets of fraction cards into a single deck. Each player needs a Unifix Operational Grid and Tray and a Blank Underlay Card.

During his or her turn, a player draws one card from the deck and constructs a model for the fraction on the grid. A player keeps the card to identify the fraction. If a fraction has already been used, the player loses that turn.

If a player displays an incorrect model for a fraction, the player who identifies the error places the correct model on his or her grid.

Play continues for ten rounds so that each row of the grid will be filled. The winner is the player who has the most cubes on his or her grid.

VARIATIONS:
Use the Unifix Rod Stamps to stamp the back of each fraction card. Shade the corresponding number of squares to make a self-checking activity. For example:

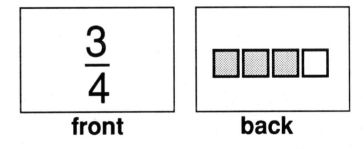

front   back

0	1	$\frac{1}{2}$
$\frac{1}{3}$	$\frac{2}{3}$	$\frac{1}{4}$
$\frac{2}{4}$	$\frac{3}{4}$	$\frac{1}{5}$
$\frac{2}{5}$	$\frac{3}{5}$	$\frac{4}{5}$
$\frac{1}{6}$	$\frac{2}{6}$	$\frac{3}{6}$
$\frac{4}{6}$	$\frac{5}{6}$	**Card Shark**

Didax Educational Resources, Inc.

NAME THAT FRACTION

Activity **16**

|---|---|

GRADE LEVEL: 3 - 4

CONCEPTS OR SKILLS:
Naming fractions, determining equivalent fractions

NUMBER OF PLAYERS:
2, small groups or entire class

MATERIALS:
Name That Fraction cards
Paper bag containing four Unifix Cubes of one color and four Unifix Cubes of a different color
Several cubes to use as markers for each player

GETTING READY:
Using card stock, make sufficient quantities of Name That Fraction Cards so that each player will have one card.

Put four Unifix Cubes of one color and four Unifix Cubes of a different color in a paper bag.

DIRECTIONS:
Several bingo games focusing on fraction names and/or equivalent fractions are possible using Unifix Cubes. Each player needs a Name That Fraction Card. The rules are the same for each game. The first player to get four cubes in a row, horizontally, vertically, or diagonally is the winner.

Game 1 (2 players)
Before beginning a game, assign each player one of the colors of cubes that are in the bag.

During his or her turn, a player takes a handful of cubes from the bag and places them in view of the other player.

Each player then determines what fraction of the cubes are of his or her particular color, and then covers, if possible, the corresponding fraction on the card.

For example, Player 1 has been assigned red cubes and Player 2 has been assigned white cubes. Player 1 takes a handful of cubes from the bag and shows two red and three white cubes.

Player 1 would cover $\frac{2}{5}$ and player 2 would cover $\frac{3}{5}$.

If necessary, a player must reduce a fraction to lowest terms ($\frac{4}{6} = \frac{2}{3}$).

After a turn, the cubes are returned to the paper bag for the next player's turn.

If a fraction is already covered or is not on a card, a player loses that turn. However, the second player may cover, if possible, his or her fraction.

Game 2 (Entire class)
The rules are the same, except a player only covers a fraction on his or her turn.

Game 3 (Small group)
Before beginning a game, players decide which color of cubes they will use to determine fractions. More than one player may select the same color.

During his or her turn, a player takes a handful of cubes and determines the fraction for his or her color. The player covers, if possible, the fraction with a cube and returns the other cubes to the paper bag.

Game 4 (Entire class)
Before beginning a game, you, or a designated player, should determine which color of cubes will be used to indicate fractions. You, or a designated player, should take a handful of cubes and display them to the class. The players determine the fraction for the selected color, and each player covers, if possible, the fraction on his or her card.

Unifix Translucent Color Squares for use on an overhead projector work well as markers for this game.

VARIATIONS:
Blank Name That Fraction cards are provided in order to extend the games to other fractions. Add additional cubes of two colors to the paper bag.

43

NAME THAT FRACTION

$\frac{2}{5}$	$\frac{2}{3}$	$\frac{3}{7}$	$\frac{1}{3}$
1	$\frac{3}{5}$	$\frac{1}{2}$	$\frac{2}{3}$
$\frac{3}{4}$	$\frac{1}{4}$	$\frac{1}{3}$	1
$\frac{1}{5}$	$\frac{4}{7}$	$\frac{4}{5}$	$\frac{1}{2}$

NAME THAT FRACTION

$\frac{4}{7}$	0	$\frac{1}{3}$	$\frac{1}{5}$
1	$\frac{2}{5}$	$\frac{2}{3}$	$\frac{1}{4}$
$\frac{3}{4}$	$\frac{3}{7}$	$\frac{1}{2}$	0
$\frac{4}{5}$	$\frac{1}{2}$	$\frac{2}{3}$	$\frac{3}{5}$

NAME THAT FRACTION

$\frac{1}{2}$	$\frac{4}{7}$	1	$\frac{2}{3}$
$\frac{1}{3}$	$\frac{1}{5}$	$\frac{3}{5}$	$\frac{1}{2}$
$\frac{1}{4}$	$\frac{3}{4}$	$\frac{4}{5}$	$\frac{3}{7}$
1	$\frac{1}{2}$	$\frac{1}{4}$	0

NAME THAT FRACTION

$\frac{1}{3}$	$\frac{1}{2}$	$\frac{3}{5}$	1
$\frac{3}{7}$	$\frac{2}{3}$	0	$\frac{1}{4}$
$\frac{2}{5}$	$\frac{1}{4}$	$\frac{1}{2}$	$\frac{2}{3}$
$\frac{1}{3}$	$\frac{4}{7}$	1	$\frac{3}{4}$

Didax Educational Resources, Inc.

NAME THAT
FRACTION

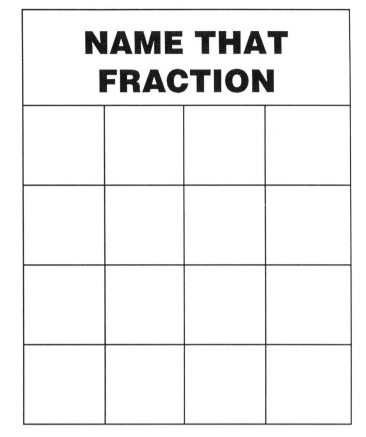

NAME THAT
FRACTION

NAME THAT
FRACTION

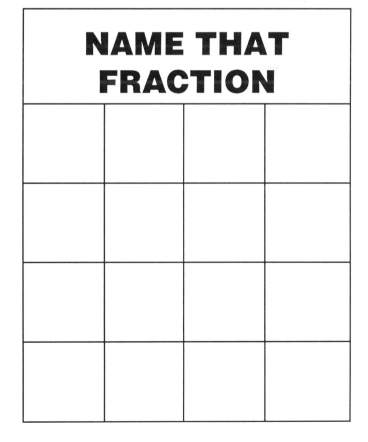

NAME THAT
FRACTION

GUESS AND MEASURE

GRADE LEVEL: 1 - 3

CONCEPTS OR SKILLS:
Estimation of length, measurement

NUMBER OF PLAYERS:
Entire class, with teacher participation

MATERIALS:
Unifix Cubes for each student
Guess and Measure Record Sheet for each student

GETTING READY:

Make copies of the Guess and Measure Record Sheet and cut them apart.

Designate ten objects to measure such as the following:

1. Foot
2. Hand span
3. Height
4. Friend's foot
5. Pencil
6. Paper width and length
7. Teacher's desk width
8. Student desk width
9. Eraser
10. Chalk
11. Door length
12. Chalkboard length
13. Meter stick
14. Window width
15. Book length and width
16. Room width

DIRECTIONS:

Ask students to write the name of the object they are measuring on the record sheet. Then ask them to guess the length of the object in Unifix Cubes and to write their guess on the corresponding line of the record sheet.

Students measure the object by placing cubes side-by-side or by making structured bars. Once the object has been measured, students record the length on the record sheet.

To add a game element, ask students to subtract their guess from the actual measure in cubes (or vice versa) and to record the difference on the corresponding line of the record sheet. Each student then finds the sum of the differences. The winner is the student who has the smallest difference.

GUESS AND MEASURE RECORD SHEET

	Object Measured	Guess	Measurement	Difference
1.	Desk	50	48 cubes	2
2.	Window	100	60 cubes	40
3.				
4.				
5.				
6.				
7.				
8.				
9.				
10.				

GUESS AND MEASURE RECORD SHEET

Object Measured	Guess	Measurement	Difference
1. _____	_____	_____	_____
2. _____	_____	_____	_____
3. _____	_____	_____	_____
4. _____	_____	_____	_____
5. _____	_____	_____	_____
6. _____	_____	_____	_____
7. _____	_____	_____	_____
8. _____	_____	_____	_____
9. _____	_____	_____	_____
10. _____	_____	_____	_____

GUESS AND MEASURE RECORD SHEET

Object Measured	Guess	Measurement	Difference
1. _____	_____	_____	_____
2. _____	_____	_____	_____
3. _____	_____	_____	_____
4. _____	_____	_____	_____
5. _____	_____	_____	_____
6. _____	_____	_____	_____
7. _____	_____	_____	_____
8. _____	_____	_____	_____
9. _____	_____	_____	_____
10. _____	_____	_____	_____

TOSS A COLOR

GRADE LEVEL: 2 - 4

CONCEPTS OR SKILLS:
Probability, graphing

NUMBER OF PLAYERS:
Small groups or entire class

MATERIALS:
Several Unifix Cubes for each player
Unifix 10 x 10 Number Tray
Blank 2 cm cube
Unifix Gummed Squares or Unifix Wax
    Crayons

GETTING READY:

Each player needs several Unifix Cubes and a Unifix 10 x 10 Number Tray.

Construct a color cube for each player. For initial activities, use only three colors of squares on a cube such as 2 red, 2 blue, and 2 white. Later, use a variety of combinations such as the following:

1. 2 red, 2 blue, 1 yellow, 1 green

2. 1 red, 1 blue, 1 yellow, 1 green, 1 black, 1 white

3. 2 black, 1 white, 1 brown, 1 light blue, 1 orange

DIRECTIONS:

For each different color on the color cube, a player will use a different channel on the 10 x 10 Tray.

Each player tosses the color cube 24 (or 30) times.

A Unifix Cube of the corresponding color is placed in a channel of the tray for each toss. When the students have completed the tosses, ask them to complete a graph of their results on graph paper. Ask the students to repeat the activity and make a new graph.

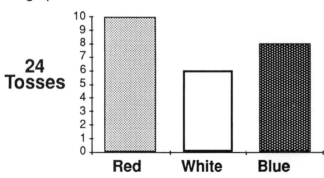

VARIATIONS:

Post each student's graphs on bulletin boards.

Question students about the results of their activity and what they observe from their graphs.

1. What color appeared the most?
2. What color appeared the least?
3. What color should appear the most?
4. What color should appear the least?

Make a large graph of the results for the entire class.

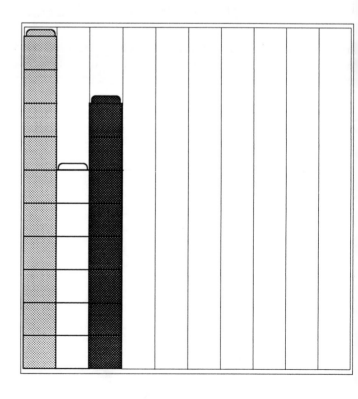

GRADE LEVEL: 2 - 4

CONCEPTS OR SKILLS:
Probability, graphing

NUMBER OF PLAYERS:
1, small groups or entire class

MATERIALS:
10 Unifix Cubes, one of each color, for each
player
Roundabout Activity Sheet and spinner
Unifix Gummed Squares

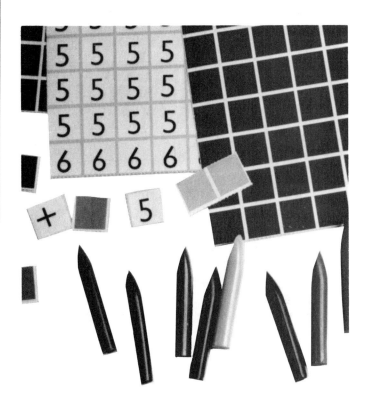

GETTING READY:
Make copies of the Roundabout Activity Sheet for
each player.

Stick a gummed square of each Unifix color on the
blank squares of the activity sheet spinner circle
and also on the squares on each side of the spinner
circle.

Each player needs 10 Unifix Cubes, one of each
color, a spinner and a pencil.

DIRECTIONS:
Roundabout can be played as a game or used
individually for tallying-graphing activities. The
rules are the same for each.

In the game format, each player during his or her
turn spins the spinner and places a Unifix Cube of
the corresponding color on the appropriate square
of the activity sheet. The player makes a tally on
his or her game sheet after each turn. If a color has
already been covered, the player loses a turn but
makes a tally for that turn. The first player to cover
all ten squares is the winner.

Individually, each player spins and covers the
colors in the same manner until all ten colors have
been covered, tallying after each spin.

Once the player has completed the sheet, he or she
totals the number of tallies.

Then ask questions such as:
Who had the least number of turns?
Who had the greatest number of turns?
What is the least number of turns that
someone could have used?
If you played the game again, about how many
turns do you think you would need?

Allow students to play additional games.

Make a bar graph of the class or group results.

VARIATIONS:
Have students play several times over a period of
time. Each student then constructs a bar graph for
his or her results.

Rather than use all the colors, place only five on the
game sheet. Play with the same rules.

ROUNDABOUT ACTIVITY SHEET

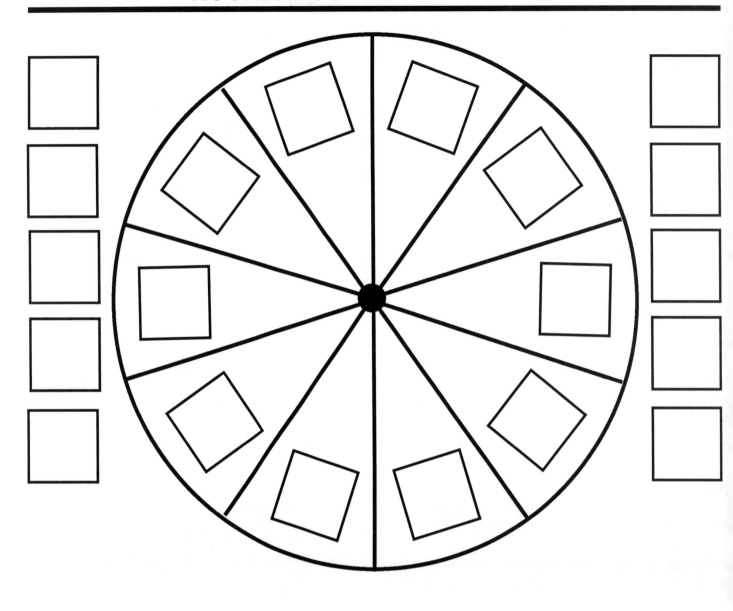

Game 1 Tally: _____

Game 2 Tally: _____

Game 3 Tally: _____

Game 4 Tally: _____

GRADE LEVEL: 2 - 4

CONCEPTS OR SKILLS:
Data collection, estimation, probability

NUMBER OF PLAYERS:
Small groups or entire class with teacher participation

MATERIALS:
1 paper bag for each group
Unifix Cubes to place in paper bag, number varies according to teacher's decision
What's in the Bag? Record Sheet

GETTING READY:

Make copies of the Record Sheet for each player.

Decide on the number of colors and the number of cubes to place in the bag. For example, beginning activities might involve ten Unifix Cubes of two colors (five red and five blue). Later activities might involve a bag containing 3 green and seven yellow.

After students have had success in determining the contents of a bag, try arrangements such as the following:

20 cubes: 10 orange, 10 brown
20 cubes: 5 white, 15 black
30 cubes: 10 red, 10 white, 10 blue
30 cubes: 5 dark blue, 10 light blue, 15 maroon

Before beginning play, demonstrate how to play to the entire group or class. One player takes a handful of cubes from the bag and records the number and color on his or her record sheet. Based on the "grab," ask the students to name the colors involved and estimate how many of each color are probably in the bag.

Place a predetermined number of cubes as suggested above in the paper bag. Give each player a record sheet. Tell the students how many cubes are in the bag and how many colors are involved. Students record these numbers at the top of the Record Sheet.

Then a designated student takes a handful of cubes from the bag and announces the number and colors of the cubes.

Each student records the "grab" on his or her record sheet and then estimates the number of cubes of each color contained in the bag. An example is shown below.

WHAT'S IN THE BAG? RECORD SHEET		
Number of Colors: __2__	Number of Unifix Cubes: __10__	
Record each grab on the blanks below.		
Grab Number of Each Color		Your Guess
1. 2 red, 2 blue		5 each
2.		
3.		
4.		
5.		
6.		
7.		
8.		
9.		
10.		

Students then state their estimates. The winner is the student who correctly determines the content of the bag. If no student guesses the correct number and color of cubes, take another handful of cubes from the bag and repeat the steps given above.

Once the contents of the bag have been determined, play again with a new set of cubes in the bag.

WHAT'S IN THE BAG? RECORD SHEET

Number of Colors: _____   Number of Unifix Cubes: _____

Record each grab on the blanks below.

Grab	Number of Each Color	Your Guess
1.	_____	_____
2.	_____	_____
3.	_____	_____
4.	_____	_____
5.	_____	_____
6.	_____	_____
7.	_____	_____
8.	_____	_____
9.	_____	_____
10.	_____	_____

WHAT'S IN THE BAG? RECORD SHEET

Number of Colors: _____   Number of Unifix Cubes: _____

Record each grab on the blanks below.

Grab	Number of Each Color	Your Guess
1.	_____	_____
2.	_____	_____
3.	_____	_____
4.	_____	_____
5.	_____	_____
6.	_____	_____
7.	_____	_____
8.	_____	_____
9.	_____	_____
10.	_____	_____

Didax Educational Resources, Inc.